THE ULTIMATE
DETROIT LIONS
TRIVIA BOOK

A Collection of Amazing Trivia Quizzes
and Fun Facts for Die-Hard Lions Fans!

Ray Walker

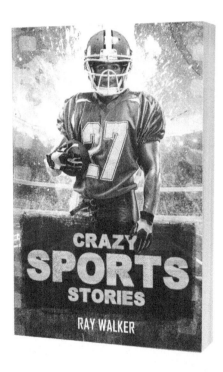

CONTENTS

INTRODUCTION

Team fandom should be inspirational. Our attachment to our favorite teams should fill us with pride, excitement, loyalty, and a sense of fulfillment in knowing that we are part of a community with many other fans who feel the same way.

Lions fans are no exception. With a long, rich history in the NFL, the Lions have inspired their supporters to strive for greatness with their tradition of colorful players, memorable eras, big moves, and unique moments.

This book is meant to be a celebration of those moments, and an examination of the collection of interesting, impressive, or important details that allow us to understand the full stories behind the players and the team.

You may use the book as you wish. Each chapter contains 20 quiz questions in a mixture of multiple-choice and true-false formats, an answer key (Don't worry, it's on a separate page!), and a section of 10 "Did You Know?" factoids about the team.

Some will use it to test themselves with the quiz questions. How much Lions history did you really know? How many of the finer points can you remember? Some will use it competitively (Isn't that the heart of sports?), waging contests with friends and fellow devotees to see who can lay claim to being the biggest fan. Some will enjoy it as a learning experience, gaining insight to enrich their fandom and add color to their understanding of their favorite team. Still others may use it to teach, sharing the wonderful anecdotes inside to inspire a new generation of fans to hop aboard the Lions bandwagon.

Whatever your purpose may be, we hope you enjoy delving into the amazing background of Detroit Lions football!

Oh…and for the record, information and statistics in this book are current up to the beginning of 2021. The Lions will surely topple more records and win more awards as the seasons pass, so keep this in mind when you're watching the next game with your friends, and someone starts a conversation with "Did you know" to share some Lions pride.

CHAPTER 1:

ORIGINS & HISTORY

QUIZ TIME!

1. In which year did the Lions franchise begin playing in the National Football League?

    a. 1920

    b. 1930

    c. 1940

    d. 1950

2. The franchise was nearly called the Detroit Motors, partially to reflect the importance of the automobile industry in Detroit's history and partially to honor a defunct rugby team from the city by that name.

    a. True

    b. False

3. How was the nickname "Lions" chosen for the team?

    a. The franchise wanted a rivalry with the nearby Chicago Bears, and felt that a lion would be a worthy challenger in a fight with a bear.

b. The name was selected in a newspaper contest from among a few possibilities with tie-ins to the founder's other businesses; Lions, Oilers, Ranchers, Linemen, or Smoke.

c. The owner wanted the team to be the "king of the NFL" and selected "Lions" since they are the "kings of the jungle."

d. At the time the team was founded, the Detroit Zoo was world famous for its jungle exhibits, which featured more captive lions than any other zoo in the world

4. In which season did the Lions begin to play in their new stadium (Ford Field) after moving from their longtime home at the Pontiac Silverdome?

   a. 1986
   b. 1994
   c. 1999
   d. 2002

5. In which city, and under which nickname, was the Detroit Lions franchise initially founded?

   a. Portsmouth Spartans (Ohio)
   b. b. Trenton Tigers (New Jersey)
   c. c. Rochester Americans (New York)
   d. d. Scranton Beavers (Pennsylvania)

6. In which season did the Lions franchise earn its first-ever playoff berth?

a. 1930

b. 1932

c. 1935

d. 1952

7. The Detroit Lions won more games than any other NFL team between 1970 and 1980.

    a. True

    b. False

8. How many times in their franchise history have the Lions won a division title?

    a. 4

    b. 8

    c. 17

    d. 25

9. Who joined offensive lineman George Christensen as Detroit's first players ever to be named to the NFL All-Pro First Team?

    a. Tailback Dutch Clark

    b. Offensive lineman Ox Emerson

    c. Quarterback Bobby Layne

    d. Running back Glenn Presnell

10. Where do the Detroit Lions rank among NFL franchises when it comes to most Super Bowls won?

    a. 2nd place overall

    b. 11th place overall

    c. Tied for 19th place overall

    d. Tied for last place overall

11. How did the Lions fare during their 50th season in Detroit?

    a. Missed the playoffs

    b. Lost in the divisional round to the San Francisco 49ers

    c. Lost in the first round to the Washington Football Team

    d. Won the championship over the Buffalo Bills

12. The longest stretch the Lions have gone without making the playoffs is 11 years, from 1971 to 1981.

    a. True

    b. False

13. Which team did the Lions face in their first-ever regular season NFL game at the Pontiac Silverdome (which resulted in a 36-10 loss)?

    a. San Diego Chargers

    b. Green Bay Packers

    c. Dallas Cowboys

    d. Minnesota Vikings

14. What were the details surrounding the Lions' first-ever shutout in Detroit?

    a. It was a 9-0 win over the New York Giants in 1934.

    b. It was a 21-0 win over the Brooklyn Dodgers in 1935.

    c. It was a 6-0 loss to the Chicago Cardinals in 1936.

    d. It was a 12-0 loss to the Cincinnati Reds in 1937.

15. Which player used the drop kick method to convert the first-ever field goal for the Lions after they moved to Detroit?

a. Tackle Jack Johnson

b. End Harry Ebding

c. Quarterback Dutch Clark

d. Fullback Ace Gutowsky

16. As of 2021, Detroit is tied with the Chicago Bears and New York Giants as the franchises that have sent more players to the Pro Bowl than any other NFL franchise.

a. True

b. False

17. How did the Lions fare in their first-ever NFL playoff run after moving to Detroit?

a. Lost in the first round to the Chicago Bears

b. Lost in the second round to the St. Louis Cardinals

c. Lost in the NFL Championship to the Cleveland Browns

d. Won the NFL Championship over the New York Giants

18. What is Detroit's franchise record for most victories recorded by the club in a single regular season?

a. 10

b. 11

c. 12

d. 13

19. What is the name of the Lions' team mascot?

a. "Leo the Lion"

b. "Motown Man"

c. "Growly McGee"

d. "Roary the Lion"

20. The Detroit football franchise has, at some point, been included in both the Western Conference and the Eastern Conference within the NFL's division of teams.

a. True

b. False

QUIZ ANSWERS

1. B – 1930

2. B – False

3. C – The owner wanted the team to be the "king of the NFL" and selected "Lions" since they are the "kings of the jungle."

4. D – 2002

5. A – Portsmouth Spartans (Ohio)

6. B – 1932

7. B – False

8. B – 8

9. A – Tailback Dutch Clark

10. D – Tied for last place overall

11. B – Lost in divisional round to San Francisco 49ers

12. B – False

13. C – Dallas Cowboys

14. A – It was a 9-0 win over the New York Giants in 1934.

15. C – Quarterback Dutch Clark

16. B – False

17. D – Won the NFL Championship over the New York Giants

18. C – 12

19. D – "Roary the Lion"

20. B – False

DID YOU KNOW?

1. The Lions franchise has played at five different stadiums during its history. For their first four seasons, they played at Universal Stadium. For another seven, they suited up at the University of Detroit. Tiger Stadium was home for about three decades, followed by the Pontiac Silverdome for just shy of that tenure, and now the Lions reside at Ford Field.

2. Detroit had been home to four professional football teams before the Lions arrived, with all four spending time in the NFL. These short-lived franchises included the Heralds, the Tigers, the Panthers, and the Wolverines.

3. Ford Field, the current home of the Lions, is actually located in downtown Detroit, which is a nice change for fans of the team, who had to commute to Pontiac, Michigan, when the team played in the Silverdome.

4. While the Lions are the anchor tenants of Ford Field, it is not their home exclusively. The arena configuration changes, varying from 65,000 seats up to about 80,000 seats. The smaller setup is generally used for football, while the larger one is implemented for basketball, wrestling, concerts, and other such events.

5. The Detroit Lions Cheerleaders are the official cheerleaders for the franchise, and have operated off and on throughout

the team's history. The team had a squad from 1963 to 1974, but shut it down at that point and did not reinstitute it until 2016.

6. The first touchdown in franchise history after the Lions moved to Detroit was actually scored on defense. A player named Father Lumpkin intercepted a pass against the New York Giants quarterback and ran it back 45 yards to put his name in the history books and secure a victory for Detroit.

7. Detroit has a few NFL rivals. The primary ones would be the Chicago Bears and Green Bay Packers, which is based on a long history of sharing a division and playing each other frequently. The Lions also have a geographical rivalry with the Cleveland Browns, known as the "Great Lakes Classic." The two teams usually meet only in the preseason, where they compete for The Barge and yearly bragging rights.

8. In the team's first season in Detroit, 1934, things could not have started off much better. Not only did the Lions shutout their first opponents, the New York Giants, in a 9-0 win, but they reeled off seven consecutive shutouts and 10 consecutive wins to start their tenure in Detroit.

9. The official fight song of the Detroit Lions is called "Gridiron Heroes." Its first use was as a celebratory song for the team in the 1930s, when it was written by the Lions' director of entertainment, Graham T. Overgard.

10. In the beginning, the franchise was founded in Portsmouth, Ohio, in 1928 and was owned by the city. Because the franchise was in difficult financial straits, it was sold to George A. Richards, a radio station owner from Michigan. Richards moved the team to Detroit and is generally considered the founder of the Lions.

CHAPTER 2:

JERSEYS & NUMBERS

QUIZ TIME!

1. When the franchise began playing in 1930 as the Portsmouth Spartans, what color scheme was used for their home and away uniforms?

    a. Green, brown, and white

    b. Blue, silver, and white

    c. Black, gold, and white

    d. Purple, gold, and white

2. The numbers 0 and 00 have been banned from circulation by Detroit's ownership, as they are seen to represent a losing attitude.

    a. True

    b. False

3. How many blue stripes are featured on the Lions' helmets, running from crown to neck?

    a. 1

    b. 2

c. 3

d. 0

4. Two Hall of Fame Detroit players each wore number 20 for a decade with the team. Who were these two players?

    a. Cornerback Lem Barney and running back Barry Sanders

    b. Running back Billy Sims and guard Sonny Liles

    c. Defensive backs Jim Steffen and Bill Stits

    d. Center Ox Emerson and tackle Lloyd Wickett

5. In which year did players' names first appear on the backs of Lions jerseys?

    a. 1950

    b. 1960

    c. 1970

    d. 1980

6. Which jersey name and number combination has proven to be among the five most popular with Lions fans on detroitlions.com, despite the player's retirement years ago?

    a. Barry Sanders's number 20

    b. Calvin Johnson's number 81

    c. Dutch Clark's number 7

    d. Bobby Layne's number 22

7. The blue jerseys worn by Detroit are often said to have been "jinxed," and the team avoids wearing them during the Super Bowl whenever the choice is theirs.

    a. True

    b. False

8. Who is the player to wear the highest numbered jersey in Lions franchise history (number 99) for the most games?

    a. Defensive end James Cribbs
    b. Linebacker Tracy Hayworth
    c. Linebacker C.J. Mosley
    d. Linebacker Richard Jordan

9. The current version of the Lions' uniform is based around which shade of blue?

    a. Royal blue
    b. Sky blue
    c. Honolulu blue
    d. Prussian blue

10. For over 50 years, fullback Jonny Olszewski was the only Lion to ever wear which of the following uniform numbers?

    a. 0
    b. 44
    c. 69
    d. 92

11. Sixteen players have worn number 88 for the Lions. Which of these players scored the most career touchdowns?

    a. Tight end T.J. Hockenson
    b. Wide receiver Mike Williams
    c. Wide receiver Scotty Anderson
    d. Tight end Charlie Sanders

12. Star linebacker Joe Schmidt is the only Lion to have ever worn the number 56 on his jersey and will continue to be the only one as his number is now retired.

    a. True
    b. False

13. Why did star quarterback Matthew Stafford choose to wear number 9 on the back of his jersey for Detroit?

    a. His hero was Washington quarterback Sonny Jurgensen, who wore number 9.
    b. He was selected 9th overall in the NFL Draft in 2009, so it felt lucky to him.
    c. He wanted number 7, but it was retired, so he chose something close to it.
    d. It was recommended by his agent, who told him that single-digit numbers help sell more jerseys to fans.

14. How many jersey numbers have the Detroit Lions retired for their former players?

    a. 2
    b. 3
    c. 5
    d. 6

15. Which player competed for the Lions for just 16 games; the shortest tenure of anyone whose number has been retired by the franchise?

    a. Tailback Dutch Clark
    b. Linebacker Mo Lewis

c. Wide receiver Chuck Hughes

d. Linebacker Joe Schmidt

16. Nine players have worn the number 1 for Detroit, and every single one of them was a quarterback.

a. True

b. False

17. Lucky number 7 has been worn by just two Lions players over the years. Which athlete wore it for the longest amount of time?

a. Center Ox Emerson

b. Quarterback Matthew Stafford

c. Running back Doak Walker

d. Tailback Dutch Clark

18. Who is the most recent Lions player to have his number retired by the club?

a. Linebacker Chris Spielman

b. Running back Barry Sanders

c. Wide receiver Calvin Johnson

d. Quarterback Bobby Layne

19. Which number did star Lions running back Doak Walker, in whose honor the NCAA gives out an award each year to the best running back in the country, wear on the back of his jersey?

a. 37

b. 11

c. 33

d. 5

20. The Lions have retired more jersey numbers than any other NFL franchise has.

    a. True
    b. False

QUIZ ANSWERS

1. D – Purple, gold, and white

2. B – False

3. C – 3

4. A – Cornerback Lem Barney and running back Barry Sanders

5. C – 1970

6. A – Barry Sanders's number 20

7. B – False

8. B – Linebacker Tracy Hayworth

9. C – Honolulu blue

10. A – 0

11. D – Tight end Charlie Sanders

12. B – False

13. C – He wanted number 7, but it was retired, so he chose something close to it.

14. D – 6

15. C – Wide receiver Chuck Hughes

16. B – False

17. D – Tailback Dutch Clark

18. B – Running back Barry Sanders

19. A – 37

20. B – False

DID YOU KNOW?

1. For four seasons, between 1948 and 1951, the Lions wore uniforms that were primarily red and black. New coach Bo McMilin decided to make the switch because of the success he'd had at Indiana University, where the Hoosiers wore those colors.

2. The Lions do not retire many numbers, but they do opt to unofficially take some numbers out of circulation. Thus far, this is how the Lions have chosen to honor wide receiver Calvin Johnson after his retirement in 2015.

3. Detroit linebacker C.J. Mosley chose to wear number 99 on his jersey because of his reverence for Hall of Fame defensive tackle Warren Sapp, who sported that number with the Tampa Bay Buccaneers.

4. When the Lions began putting uniform numbers on the sleeves of their jerseys in the 1950s, the idea was met with resistance from players. Hall of Fame offensive tackle Lou Creekmur explained that it would now be much easier for the referees to notice when the linemen were illegally holding their opponents.

5. During the 1950s, the NFL experimented with using a white football that would show up better for night games. Detroit's silver helmets were occasionally mistaken for the ball, so the team was forced to spray paint their helmets

blue when the contests were not scheduled during daylight.

6. When Reggie Bush signed with the Detroit Lions, he could not have his usual number, 22, because it was retired in honor of legendary quarterback Bobby Layne. Bush took number 21, but still frequently signed autographs with the number 22.

7. Superstition may have scared some Lions away from wearing the number 13. Only nine players in franchise history have chosen it for themselves, and six of those were with the team in the 1930s and '40s.

8. Since 1973, the NFL no longer allows players to wear jersey number 0 or 00. No Detroit Lions player ever wore 00 in the seasons prior to this change, so it will go unused in franchise history. Long snapper James Fisher did wear 0 in 2019 on the practice squad, but did not play in any actual games.

9. The highest number ever retired by the Detroit Lions is number 85, belonging to wide receiver Chuck Hughes.

10. During the 1948 season, the Lions occasionally wore a uniform with both black pants and black jerseys. These were donned by the team for games that were considered particularly important to win.

CHAPTER 3:

CATCHY NICKNAMES

QUIZ TIME!

1. By which franchise nickname were the Lions commonly referred to after head coach Jim Schwartz used the term for the team?

   a. "Silver Crush"
   b. "Jungle Kings"
   c. "Detroit Rock City"
   d. "Blue Bloods"

2. Consistent Lions wide receiver Golden Tate was often referred to as "Solid Gold" thanks to his reliability and sure hands, in combination with his first name.

   a. True
   b. False

3. The longtime home of the Lions, the "Pontiac Silverdome," took on that name officially after it had been used as a nickname for years thanks to the silver appearance of the

roof when struck by sunbeams. What was the original name of the place?

a. The Detroit Dome
b. Michigan Sports Arena
c. Pontiac Metropolitan Stadium
d. Pontiac Place

4. Which Detroit player was affectionately known by players and fans as "Megatron," because at 6'5" and 237 pounds, he was as big, strong, and fast as the villain from the cartoon show *Transformers*?

a. Offensive tackle Taylor Decker
b. Safety Glover Quin
c. Wide receiver Calvin Johnson
d. Linebacker Chris Spielman

5. Why was 170 pound Lions cornerback Jim David known around the league as "The Hatchet"?

a. He was top heavy with all of his weight in his chest and shoulders, suspended by slender legs, like the design of a hatchet.
b. Prior to his playing days in Detroit, he worked as a wood cutter in his home state of South Carolina.
c. He was sharp tongued with the press and not afraid to say something negative, whether it was about opponents or teammates.
d. He knocked out future Hall of Fame quarterbacks Y.A. Tittle and Tom Fears in back-to-back games.

6. Which of the following was the real name of the Lions legend and Hall of Fame tailback who was commonly known as "Dutch" Clark during the course of his career?

   a. Earl Harry Clark
   b. William Seymour Clark
   c. Paul David Clark
   d. Robert Foster Clark

7. Detroit quarterback Bobby Layne was known as "The Blond Bomber" during his playing days.

   a. True
   b. False

8. Why was Detroit running back Adrian Peterson given the nickname "All Day" by his parents?

   a. Because he refused to quit playing new video games and step away from the television until he had beaten every single level.
   b. Because he had so much energy that he did not stop running all day long.
   c. Because he would nag them incessantly about taking him to the local football field to play with other kids.
   d. Because he preferred to stay up throughout the night and sleep all day.

9. What was Detroit head coach George Clark also known as?

   a. "Skipper"
   b. "The Bull"

c. "Patton"

d. "Potsy"

10. Lions tight end Charlie Sanders went by which two-word nickname?

    a. "Colonel Sanders"

    b. "Charlie Deep"

    c. "Chuck Dandy"

    d. "First Down"

11. Which Lions player was known to fans and teammates by the nickname "Babytron," in reference to his performance compared to standout Lions receiver Calvin "Megatron" Johnson?

    a. Golden Tate

    b. Marvin Jones

    c. Kenny Golladay

    d. Brandon Pettigrew

12. After engaging in two memorable fights with his former Detroit teammates as a newly traded member of the Miami Dolphins, ex-Lions defensive end Ndamukong Suh earned the nickname "The Vengeful Ex."

    a. True

    b. False

13. Which current Lion is known to teammates by the nickname "The Kid" because of his lack of facial hair and youthful features?

    a. Quarterback Jared Goff

    b. Running back D'Andre Swift

    c. Defensive end Romeo Okwara

    d. Wide receiver Breshad Perriman

14. An NFL rule informally known as "The Calvin Johnson Rule," named after a famous play involving the longtime Lions wide receiver, states that a player must do what?

    a. Not become the first player to touch the ball if he has stepped out of bounds during the course of the play

    b. Refrain from taunting opposing players during the celebration of a touchdown

    c. Maintain possession of the football throughout the completion of the play

    d. Break the plane of the goal line with the football within the boundaries of the field of play, as indicated by the orange markers at each end of the goal line

15. At times during his tenure in Detroit, Lions running back Mel Farr was referred to by which rhyming nickname?

    a. "Fast Car Mel Farr"

    b. "Mel Farr Candy Bar"

    c. "Battle Scar Mel Farr"

    d. "Mel Farr Superstar"

16. Detroit quarterback Jon Kitna was called "Uncle Jonny" by his young teammates because he was brought in to provide leadership and playoff experience while demonstrating how to act as a professional athlete.

    a. True

    b. False

17. One of the more famous nicknames in Lions history is "Night Train," which was given to cornerback Dick Lane for which of the following reasons?

   a. Because of Lane's relentless motor, which meant that he never stopped pursuing ball carriers despite game situations or weather conditions.

   b. Because Lane would play "Night Train" by Jimmy Forrest frequently in his room at training camp as a rookie.

   c. Because Lane would let out a whistle similar to the sound of a train whistle just before he made impact with opposing players.

   d. Because Lane was afraid of airplanes and would travel to games on an overnight train rather than risk a plane crash.

18. Who gave star Lions running back Billy Sims the nickname "Kung Fu Billy Sims" after a play on which Sims avoided a tackle by jumping and delivering a drop kick to the head of Houston Oilers cornerback Steve Brown?

   a. Steve Brown, cornerback for the Houston Oilers
   b. Monte Clark, head coach of the Detroit Lions
   c. Chris Berman, television announcer for ESPN
   d. Bruce Lee, martial artist and Hollywood actor

19. "The Fearsome Foursome" was a nickname given to Detroit's defensive line in the 1960s, but it was also used at different times to apply to lines on all of the following teams except which one?

a. Los Angeles Rams
b. San Diego Chargers
c. New York Giants
d. Minnesota Vikings

20. Detroit running back LeRoy Erwin Gutowsky went by the same nickname as his father Assaph Gutowsky: "Ace."

a. True
b. False

QUIZ ANSWERS

1. A – "Silver Crush"

2. B – False

3. C – Pontiac Metropolitan Stadium

4. C – Wide receiver Calvin Johnson

5. D – He knocked out future Hall of Fame quarterbacks Y.A. Tittle and Tom Fears in back-to-back games.

6. A – Earl Harry Clark

7. A – True

8. B – Because he had so much energy that he did not stop running all day long.

9. D – "Potsy"

10. B – "Charlie Deep"

11. C – Kenny Golladay

12. B – False

13. A – Quarterback Jared Goff

14. C – Maintain possession of the football throughout the completion of the play

15. D – "Mel Farr Superstar"

16. B – False

17. B – Because Lane would play "Night Train" by Jimmy Forrest frequently in his room at training camp as a rookie.

18. C – Chris Berman, television announcer for ESPN

19. D – Minnesota Vikings

20. A – True

DID YOU KNOW?

1. Detroit defensive tackle Alex Karras acquired the nickname "The Mad Duck," because although he was a big man, he lacked long legs, making it seem as if he was waddling quickly rather than running.

2. Lions coach Jim Schwartz had an NFL rule nicknamed after him ("The Jim Schwartz Rule"), when he accidentally threw a challenge flag on a play that should have been reviewed by the replay booth anyway. By the original rule, the play could no longer be reviewed, but it was re-written after Schwartz's gaffe to allow the review and just charge a time out instead.

3. Dozens of colleges use the nickname "Lions," including Columbia University, which means that when Detroit selected linebacker Lou Kusserow, tight end Jerry Zawadzkas, and quarterback John Witkowski from Columbia, none of their nicknames changed upon joining the NFL.

4. In 1936, the Lions drafted a player named Bob Train from Yale University. Despite his talent and academic pedigree, it was his last name that got all the attention and earned Train the nickname "Choo Choo."

5. Lions quarterback Don Majkowski garnered the nickname "The Majik Man," in part because of his difficult last

name, and in part for his ability to engineer big plays on the field.

6. Despite numerous losses by the Lions during his tenure as the team's quarterback, Joey Harrington always maintained a positive attitude and optimistic outlook for the future. This led to local media sarcastically referring to Harrington as "Joey Blue Skies."

7. In the early days of the NFL, football was often equated with war imagery. The Lions backfield of Ace Gutowsky and Dutch Clark was no exception, and their prowess on the ground led them to be called the "Infantry Attack."

8. Offensive tackle Reilly Reiff was so large and difficult for pass rushers to get around that it felt only natural when he was dubbed "Great Barrier Reiff."

9. Detroit cornerback Dré Bly was often referred to in jest by the nickname "Ty Law." Bly was often thought to have the shortest name in the NFL, but his is actually one letter longer than longtime New England Patriots' cornerback Ty Law.

10. "Chris's Crew" was a term used to refer to the talented Lions secondary in the 1950s. Cornerback Jack Christiansen lent his name to the moniker and was the leader of a group that included Yale Larry, Jim David, Bob Smith, and Carl Karilivacz.

CHAPTER 4:

THE QUARTERBACKS

QUIZ TIME!

1. Which of these Lions quarterbacks has been sacked by opponents the most times during the span of his career (a total of 385 times sacked)?

    a. Rodney Peete

    b. Matthew Stafford

    c. Greg Landry

    d. Jon Kitna

2. Matthew Stafford holds the top four spots on the Lions' all-time list of most passing touchdowns thrown in a season.

    a. True

    b. False

3. Which quarterback has thrown the most intercepted passes in Detroit Lions franchise history?

    a. Gary Danielson

    b. Bobby Layne

   c. Matthew Stafford

   d. Eric Hipple

4. With his total of 45,109 passing yards, Matthew Stafford is the Detroit Lions' all-time career leader in this statistic. How many more yards does he have than his next closest competitor?

   a. 6

   b. 1,241

   c. 8,700

5. 29,399

6. Which Lions player set the franchise record for most passing yards in a season by a Detroit quarterback, with 5,038; the only one ever to crack 5,000?

   a. Matthew Stafford

   b. Jon Kitna

   c. Scott Mitchell

   d. Joey Harrington

7. How many players that have played quarterback for Detroit are among the 22 Lions who have been elected to the Pro Football Hall of Fame?

   a. 1

   b. 2

   c. 3

   d. 6

8. Matthew Stafford has played more games at quarterback for the Lions than any other player.

a. True

b. False

9. One journeyman Lions quarterback has been a part of 13 NFL teams, more than any other franchise leader. Who was this well-travelled player?

a. Ty Detmer

b. Matt Cassel

c. Josh Johnson

d. Jeff Garcia

10. Which Lion was the youngest player in the team's history to start at quarterback, at just 21 years old?

a. Frank Tripucka in 1949

b. Greg Landry in 1969

c. Rodney Peete in 1989

d. Matthew Stafford in 2009

11. Which new Detroit quarterback was acquired from the Los Angeles Rams when franchise quarterback Matthew Stafford was traded to Los Angeles in 2021?

a. Jared Goff

b. Sam Bradford

c. Case Keenum

d. Deshaun Watson

12. How old was Lions quarterback Frank Reich when he retired from his playing days in the NFL?

a. 28 years old

b. 33 years old

c. 37 years old

d. 41 years old

13. Lions quarterback Matthew Stafford named previous quarterback Jon Kitna as the godfather when his daughter Beckett was born in 2014.

a. True

b. False

14. Which of the following is NOT a World Football League team that quarterback Gary Danielson played for before his career took off with the Lions?

a. San Antonio Dust Devils

b. Charlotte Hornets

c. New York Stars

d. Chicago Winds

15. Hall of Fame quarterback Bobby Layne was traded by which three teams before blossoming in Detroit with the Lions?

a. Philadelphia Eagles, Green Bay Packers, and Boston Yanks

b. New York Giants, Los Angeles Rams, and Chicago Cardinals

c. Washington Redskins, Baltimore Colts, and San Francisco 49ers

d. Pittsburgh Steelers, Chicago Bears, and New York Bulldogs

16. Lions leader Greg Landry holds the franchise's record for most rushing yards in a season by a quarterback, which he set in 1971. How many yards did he rack up?

    a. 312
    b. 530
    c. 808
    d. 1,265

17. Quarterback Daunte Culpepper has won both a College Football national championship and an NFL Super Bowl championship (though, not with the Lions).

    a. True
    b. False

18. Which of the following descriptors was used by *Sports Illustrated* magazine in 1995 in reference to Lions quarterback Bobby Layne?

    a. "A blue collar player from a blue collar town on a blue collar team"
    b. "The Mickey Mantle of the NFL"
    c. "The toughest quarterback who ever lived"
    d. "A man who never met a pass, a drink, or a lady that he didn't like"

19. Detroit quarterback Joey Harrington was also a talented jazz pianist who sat in on stage with all of the following musical artists except which one?

    a. Blues Traveler
    b. Jason Mraz

c. Third Eye Blind

d. Pearl Jam

20. How many times did prolific Lions Hall of Fame quarterback Bobby Layne throw for 20 (or more) touchdowns in a single season for Detroit?

    a. 0

    b. 1

    c. 4

    d. 7

21. Among quarterbacks who have started at least five games with Detroit, Tom Dublinski has the highest interception percentage, with 7.5% of his passes thrown being picked off.

    a. True

    b. False

QUIZ ANSWERS

1. B – Matthew Stafford

2. B – False

3. C – Matthew Stafford

4. D – 29,399

5. A – Matthew Stafford

6. B – 2

7. A – True

8. C – Josh Johnson

9. D – Matthew Stafford in 2009

10. A – Jared Goff

11. C – 37 years old

12. B – False

13. A – San Antonio Dust Devils

14. D – Pittsburgh Steelers, Chicago Bears, and New York Bulldogs

15. B – 530

16. B – False

17. C – "The toughest quarterback who ever lived"

18. D – Pearl Jam

19. B – 1

20. A – True

DID YOU KNOW?

1. Karl Sweetan owns the longest passing play in Lions history. He dropped back and found talented receiver Pat Studstill for a 99-yard touchdown toss that thrilled the fans, but could not help Detroit beat the Baltimore Colts during a 45-14 loss in 1966.

2. No Lions quarterback (with a minimum of 50 passes thrown) has ever been able to complete 70% of his passes in a season. The most accurate field general was Matthew Stafford, who came the closest in 2015, when he hit 67.2%.

3. Jon Kitna could have used some better blocking when he became the Lions quarterback in 2006. He was sacked a whopping 63 times when he dropped back to pass; the highest total in Detroit history.

4. Quarterback Earl Morrall had interesting bookends surrounding his playing career with Detroit. Before his time in the NFL, while attending Michigan State University, Morrall played for the Spartans baseball team as a shortstop in the College World Series. Later, after his retirement, Morrall was elected as the mayor of Davie, Florida.

5. Detroit quarterback Matthew Stafford has served the longest tenure as Lions quarterback. Stafford spent a dozen seasons at the beginning of his career with the franchise before being traded to the Los Angeles Rams in 2021.

6. Hall of Fame Lions quarterback Bobby Layne was drafted by the Pittsburgh Steelers, but actually played for three other NFL franchises over the course of a decade (including eight years in Detroit) before ever suiting up for Pittsburgh.

7. Matthew Stafford's accuracy shone through for the Lions in 2015 when Stafford became the first quarterback in NFL history to complete over 60% of his passes in every single game.

8. In retirement, Lions quarterback Scott Mitchell gained a lot of weight, reaching a high of 366 pounds. This led him to appear on the reality television show *The Biggest Loser*, where he worked himself down to 240 pounds by the end of the show.

9. In 2016, Detroit quarterback Matthew Stafford was more clutch than anyone, helping the Lions to comebacks in the fourth quarter and leading game-winning drives in eight of the team's 16 games, both of which are NFL records.

10. The two most highly regarded quarterbacks in Lions history, Bobby Layne and Matthew Stafford, lived on the same street in Texas and went to the same high school, over 60 years apart.

CHAPTER 5:

THE PASS CATCHERS

QUIZ TIME!

1. Eight wide receivers have recorded over 30 career touchdown catches for the Lions. Which one of them has the most?

    a. Marvin Jones
    b. Herman Moore
    c. Johnnie Morton
    d. Calvin Johnson

2. No one in Lions history is within 200 receptions of Calvin Johnson at the top of Detroit's record book.

    a. True
    b. False

3. Who is the Lions' single-season leader in receiving touchdowns scored, with 16?

    a. Cloyce Box
    b. Kenny Golladay

    c. Herman Moore

    d. Calvin Johnson

4. Who holds the all-time career franchise record for receiving yardage for the Lions?

    a. Calvin Johnson

    b. Brett Perriman

    c. Golden Tate

    d. Herman Moore

5. Lions wide receiver Earl McCullouch earned a world record in 1967 that still has not been broken. Which record does McCullouch hold?

    a. Highest height cleared in a pole vault

    b. Furthest javelin thrown to hit a bullseye when landing

    c. Fastest time in the 4 x 110 yard relay

    d. Most touchdowns scored in a single football game

6. Only one Lion with at least 100 receptions has averaged 20 yards per catch over his career. Which player showed this amazing big play ability?

    a. Cloyce Box

    b. Calvin Johnson

    c. Earl McCullouch

    d. Leonard Thompson

7. During a game in 1994 against rival Green Bay Packers, Lions wide receiver Brett Perriman converted two two-point conversions, making him the first NFL player ever to do so.

a. True

b. False

8. Which Lions pass catcher has played 175 NFL games with the franchise; more than any other?

a. Tight end Jim Gibbons

b. Wide receiver Herman Moore

c. Tight end Charlie Sanders

d. Wide receiver Leonard Thompson

9. Three pass catchers have over 450 career receptions for the Detroit Lions. Which of the following players is NOT among that club?

a. Brett Perriman

b. Calvin Johnson

c. Herman Moore

d. Johnnie Morton

10. Despite all his accomplishments, Calvin Johnson has more career fumbles than any other Lions wide receiver. How many times did he cough up the ball?

a. 8

b. 14

c. 33

d. 42

11. At the end of the 2020 NFL season, the Lions had eight wide receivers under contract for 2021. Which one of those wide receivers earned the highest salary, at $2.25 million?

a. Geronimo Allison

b. Quintez Cephus

c. Breshad Perriman

d. Tyrell Williams

12. Lions receiver Mohamed Sanu once put out an initial public offering for stock on himself. The unusual venture allowed shareholders to speculate on Sanu's future earnings. Sanu opened at $10 per share and sold over 150,000 shares.

a. True

b. False

13. How many Lions tight ends have caught over 250 passes for the club during their careers?

a. 1: Charlie Sanders

b. 2: Charlie Sanders and Brandon Pettigrew

c. 3: Charlie Sanders, Brandon Pettigrew, and Jim Gibbons

d. 5: Charlie Sanders, Brandon Pettigrew, Jim Gibbons, David Hill, and Eric Ebron

14. Which two teammates posted the highest combined receiving yardage total in a season for the Lions, at 3,174?

a. Calvin Johnson and Golden Tate in 2014

b. Marvin Jones and Kenny Golladay in 2018

c. Roy Williams and Mike Furrey in 2006

d. Herman Moore and Brett Perriman in 1995

15. Which of the following NFL records does Lions Hall-of-Famer Calvin Johnson NOT hold, or at least share with another player?

    a. Most games in one season with over 100 receiving yards
    b. Most games in a row with over 100 receiving yards
    c. Most receiving yards in a single season
    d. Most catches in the overtime period of a single game

16. Wide receiver Herman Moore played frequently on Thanksgiving Day as a member of the Lions, and still owns the NFL records for most catches (61) and receiving yardage (965) recorded on Thursdays.

    a. True
    b. False

17. Two Lions receivers became the first duo in the NFL to catch over 100 passes each during the same season. Who were these pioneers?

    a. Kenny Golladay and Marvin Jones
    b. Calvin Johnson and Roy Williams
    c. Herman Moore and Brett Perriman
    d. Freddie Scott and Leonard Thompson

18. Which Lion recorded the most catches in one season for the team when he hauled in 123 passes for the squad?

    a. Wide receiver Herman Moore
    b. Wide receiver Calvin Johnson
    c. Tight end Brandon Pettigrew
    d. Wide receiver Golden Tate

19. Which two teammates posted the highest touchdown reception total in a season for the Lions, converting 23 passes into scores?

   a. Cloyce Box and Leon Hart in 1952
   b. Terry Barr and Gail Cogdill in 1963
   c. Herman Moore and Brett Perriman in 1995
   d. Both B and C

20. More Detroit Lions tight ends have led the NFL in receiving yards for a season by a tight end than their counterparts on any other team.

   a. True
   b. False

QUIZ ANSWERS

1. D – Calvin Johnson

2. B – False

3. D – Calvin Johnson

4. A – Calvin Johnson

5. C – Fastest time in the 4 x 110 yard relay

6. A – Cloyce Box

7. A – True

8. D – Wide receiver Leonard Thompson

9. A – Brett Perriman

10. B – 14

11. C – Breshad Perriman

12. A – True

13. C – 3: Charlie Sanders, Brandon Pettigrew, and Jim Gibbons

14. D – Herman Moore and Brett Perriman in 1995

15. D – Most catches in the overtime period of a single game

16. B – False

17. C – Herman Moore and Brett Perriman

18. A – Wide receiver Herman Moore

19. D – Both B and C

20. B – False

DID YOU KNOW?

1. Lions receiver Anquan Boldin ranks ninth on the all-time list for most receptions in the NFL. Boldin caught 1,076 passes, just two behind Terrell Owens for eighth place, and slightly ahead of Reggie Wayne, who sits behind Boldin in the 10th spot.

2. The single-game record for most receptions in Detroit Lions history was actually set twice. Herman Moore reeled in 14 passes against the Chicago Bears in 1995 to set the mark, and Calvin Johnson matched it in 2013 against the Dallas Cowboys

3. Tight end Charlie Sanders was a Detroit Lion for life. When his playing days were over, Sanders continued to work for the team in several capacities. Among his many jobs with the Lions, Sanders was a radio broadcaster, assistant coach, scout, assistant director of pro personnel, community relations specialist, and spokesperson.

4. The first-ever winner of the All-Iron Award, given out by CBS broadcaster Phil Simms for the top performance by a player on Thanksgiving Day, was Detroit linebacker Stephen Boyd, who was deemed the recipient in 1998.

5. Detroit wide receiver Golden Tate was actually a talented athlete in more sports than just football. Tate was drafted by a Major League Baseball team not once, but twice, with

the Arizona Diamondbacks selecting him in 2007 and the San Francisco Giants claiming him in 2010 after Tate did not sign a contract with Arizona.

6. Wide receiver Marvin Jones actually holds the single-game touchdown catch record for two teams. Six years before Jones caught four touchdowns for Detroit against the Minnesota Vikings to set the Lions' franchise record, Jones also caught four touchdowns in a game for Cincinnati against the New York Jets to establish the Bengals' record as well.

7. Popular Lions wide receiver Nate Burleson once broke his arm in a car accident after becoming distracted while trying to keep a pizza off of one of his seats. It wasn't all bad for Burleson though, as DiGiorno's provided Burleson with a yearlong supply of free pizza after the crash.

8. In retirement, Detroit wide receiver Calvin Johnson opened a dispensary for medical cannabis in Michigan. Johnson sits on the board of directors for the Michigan Cannabis Industry Association and has teamed up with researchers at Harvard University to learn more about the effects of cannabis on dealing with pain.

9. Lions wide receiver Roy Williams was not the only player by that name in the NFL. During his career, Williams faced off against a Dallas Cowboys safety with the same name. In 2008, Williams (the receiver) was traded to Dallas where both players suited up for the same squad.

10. Brett Perriman was an excellent wide receiver for Detroit in the 1990s, but one of his proudest moments came decades later when his son, Breshad Perriman, also joined the Lions as a wide receiver in 2021.

CHAPTER 6:

RUNNING WILD

QUIZ TIME!

1. Who holds the Lions' single-season franchise rushing yardage record after racking up 2,053 yards on the ground; the only time a Detroit running back has broken the 2,000-yard barrier?

    a. Barry Sanders
    b. Billy Sims
    c. James Stewart
    d. Reggie Bush

2. It is a Lions tradition for every running back to tap his helmet against the helmets of the starting offensive linemen following the warm-up before a game.

    a. True
    b. False

3. Which running back has accumulated the most carries for Detroit (125) without ever scoring a rushing touchdown?

a. Horace King

b. Camp Wilson

c. Ron Rivers

d. Elmer Schaake

4. Which of the following did Lions running back Kevin Jones NOT do after his retirement from the NFL?

a. Earn a bachelor's degree from Virginia Tech University

b. Move to Switzerland to become an intern at a furniture company

c. Join a sailing crew aboard a 68 foot racing yacht

d. Star in commercials for Detroit-based Little Caesars Pizza

5. How many running backs have carried the ball over 1,000 times for the Lions?

a. 0

b. 1

c. 2

d. 4

6. No Lions running back with at least 30 games played has averaged over 100 yards per game during his career. Barry Sanders is the closest; what is his average?

a. 88.5

b. 91.3

c. 96.4

d. 99.8

7. Barry Sanders has 99 rushing touchdowns with the Lions, which is more than the next three highest Detroit running backs combined.

   a. True

   b. False

8. In which season did Barry Sanders record an astonishing 6.1 yards per carry for Detroit?

   a. 1995

   b. 1997

   c. 2001

   d. 2003

9. Which Detroit running back (with at least 300 carries) has the highest career yards gained per attempt, with 5.2?

   a. Ernie Caddel

   b. Barry Sanders

   c. Doak Walker

   d. Nick Pietrosante

10. Lions rusher Ace Gutowsky later became a championship level card player in which of the following games?

    a. Poker

    b. Euchre

    c. Canasta

    d. Bridge

11. How many of the Lions' top 10 seasons for rushing touchdowns were recorded by the great Barry Sanders?

a. 3

b. 5

c. 7

d. 10

12. In 2011, Lions running back Kevin Smith starred in a short film called *12 Angry Dudes*, which was directed by a famous filmmaker also named Kevin Smith.

    a. True

    b. False

13. Which Detroit running back has the most career fumbles, with 41?

    a. Rick Kane

    b. Dexter Bussey

    c. Billy Sims

    d. Barry Sanders

14. Which Lion had the highest single-season rushing yards per game, with a whopping 128.3?

    a. Mel Farr

    b. Billy Sims

    c. Barry Sanders

    d. Kerryon Johnson

15. Which of the following is NOT true about Lions legend Barry Sanders's 12-game junior season with the Oklahoma State Cowboys in 1988?

    a. He rushed for 2,850 yards that year.

    b. He scored 42 rushing touchdowns that year.

c. He led his team to a National Championship that year.

d. He won the Heisman Trophy as college football's best player that year.

16. Lions running back Billy Sims once offered to play for the team without a contract, permitting Detroit executives to pay him whatever they decided his value was worth.

a. True

b. False

17. In retirement, after a decade-long playing career with the Lions, running back Dexter Bussey worked for the NFL for two decades in which of the following positions?

a. Health and safety liaison

b. Line judge

c. Uniform inspector

d. Timekeeper

18. Which of the following is NOT an NFL record held by dynamic Lions running back Barry Sanders?

a. Most career games (25) with over 150 yards rushing

b. Most career touchdown runs (15) that were 50 yards or longer

c. Most career rushing yards lost (1,114) on negative carries

d. Most career tackles broken (2,307) by opposing players

19. Detroit running back Ace Gutowsky was once tripped by an opposing coach in order to prevent a touchdown

during an NFL Championship game. Which coach stuck his foot out as Gutowsky raced down the sidelines?

   a. Lud Wray of the Boston Braves

   b. George Halas of the Chicago Bears

   c. Curly Lambeau of the Green Bay Packers

   d. Steve Owen of the New York Giants

20. During his 10 seasons in the NFL, Detroit superstar Barry Sanders was invited to the Pro Bowl every single year.

   a. True

   b. False

QUIZ ANSWERS

1. A – Barry Sanders

2. B – False

3. D – Elmer Schaake

4. D – Star in commercials for Detroit-based Little Caesars Pizza

5. D – 4

6. D – 99.8

7. A – True

8. B – 1997

9. A – Ernie Caddel

10. D – Bridge

11. C – 7

12. B – False

13. D – Barry Sanders

14. C – Barry Sanders

15. C – He led his team to a National Championship that year.

16. A – True

17. C – Uniform inspector

18. D – Most career tackles broken (2,307) by opposing players

19. B – George Halas of the Chicago Bears

20. A – True

DID YOU KNOW?

1. Six running backs that have played for the Lions have been enshrined in the Pro Football Hall of Fame. The most recent was the legendary Barry Sanders, who was elected in 2004.

2. In retirement, Detroit rusher Billy Sims attempted several business ventures that failed, including a radio station, a nightclub, a dry cleaning business, and an auto parts maker. Sims eventually made the decision to sell his Heisman Trophy, though part of the agreement was that he had the right to buy it back by paying 8.5% interest along with the original cost.

3. Eleven times in NFL history, a running back has scored 20 or more rushing touchdowns in a single season. No Lions back has ever reached the threshold. Barry Sanders was the closest, when in 1991, he scored 16 times on the ground.

4. Running back Mel Farr took a lesson from Detroit's ownership and invested in Ford dealerships during his retirement. At one point, in 1998, Farr's collection of dealerships was considered the biggest company in the nation that was owned by an African-American.

5. Barry Sanders made an instant impact with the Detroit Lions. On his first regular season carry, Sanders took off

for an 18-yard gain. On his first regular season drive, he scored a rushing touchdown. At the end of his first season, Sanders was named Offensive Rookie of the Year and finished second overall to the Kansas City Chiefs' Christian Okoye in rushing yards and second to the Rams' Greg Bell in touchdowns.

6. Running back James Stewart had his career cut short as part of a bounty program run by notorious coach Gregg Williams. Buffalo Bills safety Coy Wire admitted, "I shattered James Stewart's shoulder and he never played again. I was showered with praise for that. It's a shame that's how it was. Now I see how wrong that was."

7. The first Detroit Lion who broke the 1,000-yard barrier in an NFL season was Steve Owens. This happened in 1971, Owens's second year with the club, when he put up 1,035 yards on the ground.

8. Early retirement has struck down perhaps the two greatest Detroit running backs in history. Billy Sims was a dominant player for five years before an injury to his right knee caused him to miss two full seasons and struggle with rehabilitation before hanging up his cleats for good. Barry Sanders gave up football early of his own accord, and while still at the top of his game, despite being within striking distance of Walter Payton's career NFL rushing record.

9. When franchise running back Nick Pietrosante left Detroit, he signed with the Cleveland Browns and had

some very big shoes to fill, as the legendary Jim Brown had retired during that offseason. Pietrosante could not compare, however, and retired after two seasons.

10. Detroit great Barry Sanders is the only NFL player to appear on the cover of two video games in the popular EA Sports *Madden* series. Interestingly, Sanders appeared on both covers *after* his playing career was finished. He made the cover in 2000 in the background behind John Madden, and was voted onto it again for *Madden NFL 25*, an anniversary edition celebrating the game's greats.

CHAPTER 7:

IN THE TRENCHES

QUIZ TIME!

1. One Lions defender recorded 5.5 sacks in a single game against the Tampa Bay Buccaneers, while no one else has more than four in a single contest. Who sits atop the team's leaderboard?

    a. Defensive tackle Ndamukong Suh
    b. Defensive end Robert Porcher
    c. Defensive end William Gay
    d. Defensive tackle Luther Elliss

2. The 2016 Detroit Lions hold the NFL record for the heaviest combined weight of all starting offensive and defensive linemen.

    a. True
    b. False

3. Who is the Lions' all-time franchise leader in sacks, having taken down opposing quarterbacks 95.5 times?

a. Defensive end Robert Porcher

b. Linebacker Mike Cofer

c. Defensive end Ezekiel Ansah

d. Defensive tackle Shaun Rogers

4. Which offensive lineman did the Lions select highest in the NFL Entry Draft, using a 5th overall pick to add the stout blocker to their team?

a. Center Alex Wojciechowicz

b. Tackle Lomas Brown

c. Guard Sid Wagner

d. Center Joe Watson

5. Which offensive lineman has played more games on the offensive side of the Lions' line of scrimmage than anyone else?

a. Center Don Muhlbach

b. Tackle Jeff Backus

c. Center Dominic Raiola

d. Guard Bob Kowalkowski

6. Which defensive lineman has played more games on the defensive side of the Lions' line of scrimmage than anyone else?

a. Defensive end Darris McCord

b. Defensive tackle Alex Karras

c. Defensive end Robert Porcher

d. Defensive tackle Doug English

7. Lions defensive lineman Alex Karras had two brothers, Lou and Ted, who also played in the NFL. Ted spent time with Detroit as well, including in 1965, when both Karras brothers played on the Lions offensive line.

   a. True
   b. False

8. Which Lions defender showed the best nose for the ball, by leading the team in most career forced fumbles?

   a. Cornerback Dré Bly
   b. Defensive end Robert Porcher
   c. Linebacker Chris Spielman
   d. Defensive end Cliff Avril

9. A quarterback tops the record books for most fumbles recovered for the Lions, but they tend to be cleaning up their own mess. Which three defenders are tied for creating the most turnovers for Detroit by scooping up an opponent's fumble?

   a. Defensive tackle Alex Karras and defensive ends William Gay and Kalimba Edwards
   b. Safety Bennie Blades, linebacker Jimmy Williams, and defensive tackle Roger Brown
   c. Cornerback Lem Barney and linebackers Chris Spielman and Joe Schmidt
   d. Safety Dick Jauron and linebackers Wayne Walker and Sonny Gandee

10. Lineman Dominic Raiola played his entire NFL career with the Detroit Lions after they chose him with the 50th overall selection in the 2001 NFL Draft. How long did that career last?

    a. 5 years
    b. 8 years
    c. 11 years
    d. 14 years

11. Lions mainstay Jeff Backus played over 190 NFL games with the club. Where does he rank in games played all time for Detroit?

    a. 2nd all time
    b. 5th all time
    c. Tied for 7th all time
    d. 12th all time

12. The Detroit Lions' internal award for Man of the Year is named after former defensive end Robert Porcher thanks to his philanthropy and community involvement.

    a. True
    b. False

13. Which current Lions defensive lineman has the longest tenure in Detroit?

    a. Tackle Nick Williams
    b. End Trey Flowers
    c. End Romeo Okwara
    d. End Charles Harris

14. Which of the following facts about Lions offensive lineman Taylor Decker is NOT true?

 a. He went to elementary school, high school, and college in Ohio.

 b. He played every offensive snap for Detroit during his rookie season.

 c. He skipped his senior year of college eligibility to enter the NFL Draft.

 d. He caught a touchdown pass from Lions quarterback Matthew Stafford.

15. Center Dominic Raiola once admitted to taking a cheap shot at the knees of New England Patriots defensive tackle Zach Moore. What inspired Raiola to do so?

 a. The Patriots ran up the score with a touchdown when they could have knelt on the ball and ended the game.

 b. Moore had spit at Lions quarterback Matthew Stafford after tackling him on the previous play.

 c. Moore had engaged in a Twitter battle with Raiola's wife in the week prior to the game.

 d. The Patriots had knocked Lions wide receiver Calvin Johnson out of the game with a play that Raiola considered questionable.

16. Detroit defensive lineman Alex Karras spent some time wrestling professionally and once took on famous opponent "Dick the Bruiser" in a match.

 a. True

 b. False

17. Which of the following is NOT a business started by former Lions defensive end Robert Porcher after his NFL retirement?

    a. Sweet Georgia Brown
    b. Seldom Blues
    c. Detroit Breakfast House & Grill
    d. Porches by Porcher

18. Which former Lions offensive tackle became a radio broadcaster for Detroit games after working as an analyst for ESPN?

    a. Jeff Backus
    b. Rocky Freitas
    c. Lomas Brown
    d. Chris Dieterich

19. In retirement from his playing career, former Lions center Dominic Raiola was hired in which position with Detroit?

    a. Amateur scout
    b. Director of community relations
    c. Head coach
    d. Strength and conditioning assistant coach

20. Lions offensive tackle Lomas Brown once admitted to the media that he purposely allowed opposing rusher Sean Jones of the Green Bay Packers to slip past him, in order to injure Detroit quarterback Scott Mitchell and force Mitchell's removal from the game.

    a. True
    b. False

QUIZ ANSWERS

1. C – Defensive end William Gay

2. B – False

3. A – Defensive end Robert Porcher

4. D – Center Joe Watson

5. A – Center Don Muhlbach

6. C – Defensive end Robert Porcher

7. A – True

8. B – Defensive end Robert Porcher

9. C – Cornerback Lem Barney and linebackers Chris Spielman and Joe Schmidt

10. D – 14 years

11. B – 5th all time

12. A – True

13. C – End Romeo Okwara

14. C – He skipped his senior year of college eligibility to enter the NFL Draft.

15. A – The Patriots ran up the score with a touchdown when they could have knelt on the ball and ended the game.

16. A – True

17. D – Porches by Porcher

18. C – Lomas Brown

19. D – Strength and conditioning assistant coach

20. A – True

DID YOU KNOW?

1. A defensive lineman holds the Detroit record for most safeties created. Tackle Doug English racked up four of them throughout his Lions career.

2. For 13 years, Darris McCord lined up along the defensive front for the Detroit Lions. McCord moved between tackle and end, but never left the Lions and rarely came off the field. He set the team's record for most games played before his retirement; although, that mark has since been passed.

3. Defensive end Larry Hand was nimble for a big man. Hand picked off five passes during 13 seasons with the Lions and was able to return three of the five for touchdowns.

4. Pro Football Hall-of-Famer Alex Karras was a talented defensive lineman for Detroit, but his talents extended off the field as well. Karras went on to act in many projects, including landing the memorable roles of being saved by Hawkeye Pierce on *M*A*S*H*, as Mongo in the movie *Blazing Saddles,* and as George Papadopolis in the television show *Webster,* among others.

5. Lions defensive lineman Kelvin Pritchett took voting very seriously. During the 2004 presidential election, Pritchett meant to vote using an absentee ballot, but when he could not obtain one, he flew to his home in Jacksonville, Florida, voted, and flew back to Detroit on the same day.

6. In the old days, NFL players often worked other jobs during the offseason to make ends meet. Four-time Pro Bowl Lions center Ed Flanagan, for example, had three: selling steel, beer, and real estate during the downtime.

7. Star defensive lineman Alex Karras was once suspended by the NFL for a year because he had gambled on NFL games. Upon his reinstatement, Karras was named a Lions captain, but refused to call heads or tails for the pregame coin toss as he had promised to no longer gamble.

8. Lions offensive tackle Lomas Brown was a model of consistency for the franchise, playing in a whopping 164 games for the team and starting 163 of them in over a decade with the team.

9. The "Fearsome Foursome" was a defensive line that took the field for Detroit in the early 1960s. That line consisted of ends Darris McCord and Sam Williams, plus tackles Alex Karras and Roger Brown. The defense posted 50 sacks in 1964 and 49 sacks the following year.

10. Offensive tackle Jeff Backus was a hometown boy. Backus was born in Michigan, went to the University of Michigan and was thrilled to be drafted by the Detroit Lions. Backus signed two contracts with Detroit and never played a snap for another NFL team.

CHAPTER 8:

THE BACK SEVEN

QUIZ TIME!

1. Which Lions cornerback is the franchise's all-time leader in interceptions, with 62?

   a. Lem Barney

   b. Yale Larry

   c. James Hunter

   d. Dick LeBeau

2. During the poker craze of the 2010s, members of Detroit's secondary and linebacking corps held a weekly game where, rather than playing for money, the losers had to tweet embarrassing things about themselves or flattering things about the winners.

   a. True

   b. False

3. One Lions player has a big lead for the team's most interceptions returned for a touchdown, with seven career scores in this fashion. Who is he?

a. Safety Jack Christiansen

b. Cornerback Dick LeBeau

c. Cornerback Lem Barney

d. Linebacker Joe Schmidt

4. Although sacks are usually not a high priority for defensive backs in most coaching systems, one Lions defensive back excelled at this skill, putting up 6.5 sacks in his career, more than one per year while playing for Detroit. Who is he?

a. Safety Ron Rice

b. Cornerback Dré Bly

c. Safety Louis Delmas

d. Safety Tavon Wilson

5. The initials in talented Lions cornerback R.W. McQuarters's name actually stand for what?

a. Raymond Wayne

b. Roderick Wallace

c. Robert William

d. Running Wild

6. Which of the following is NOT an actual celebration of a sack performed by Lions linebacker Stephen Tulloch after taking down an opposing quarterback?

a. Firing an imaginary arrow into the air and watching a teammate pretend to be struck in the heart with it

b. "Tebowing" – kneeling down to pray, after actually sacking the gesture's namesake, Tim Tebow

c. Running immediately back to the line of scrimmage for the next play

d. Tearing his ACL while leaping and flexing after sacking Green Bay Packers quarterback Aaron Rodgers

7. Over the past four seasons, between 2017 and 2020, four different players have finished each season as the Lions leading tackler.

   a. True
   b. False

8. Which of the following is NOT true about versatile Hall of Fame Lions defensive back Lem Barney?

   a. He played quarterback on his high school team.
   b. In the offseason, he routinely practiced basketball with the Harlem Globetrotters.
   c. In addition to defensive back, he also served as the punter for the Lions.
   d. He led the NFL in interceptions during his rookie season in the league.

9. After his playing days with the Lions ended, Hall of Fame defensive back Dick Lane remained with the team in which of the following positions?

   a. Play by play announcer on WJRZ for the Lions' radio broadcasts
   b. Defensive backs assistant coach
   c. Amateur area scout for the Midwest region
   d. Special assistant to William Clay Ford Sr., Detroit's owner

10. Which of the following is NOT true about the career of Lions linebacker Tahir Whitehead?

    a. He caused a fumble on special teams in his first game with the Lions.

    b. He grabbed both of his first two career interceptions in the same game.

    c. He did not see the field for a single defensive snap during his first two years with Detroit.

    d. He played 23 snaps as a tight end during various games with the Lions.

11. Lions mainstay Wayne Walker played over 200 NFL games as a linebacker with the club. Where does he rank in games played all time for Detroit?

    a. 2nd overall

    b. 4th overall

    c. Tied for 6th overall

    d. Tied for 8th overall

12. Years after his playing and broadcasting careers were both over, Detroit linebacker Chris Spielman became a special assistant to the team's chairman and president and CEO.

    a. True

    b. False

13. Which of the following options did Lions linebacker DeAndre Levy once describe as his "proudest moment"?

    a. Being drafted into the NFL with the 76th overall pick by the Detroit Lions in 2009

b. Retiring with enough money to buy a house for himself, his parents, and each of his three kids in 2016

c. Breaking Penn State coach Joe Paterno's shin in a sideline accident in college

d. Making Second Team All-Pro in his best year, 2014

14. Which of these current Lions linebackers has been with the team for four seasons; the longest current tenure in that position group for Detroit?

    a. Alex Anzalone
    b. Jamie Collins Sr.
    c. Shaun Dion Hamilton
    d. Jalen Reeves-Maybin

15. Which of the following facts about Lions cornerback Don Doll is NOT true?

    a. He was the only NFL player to record a minimum of 10 interceptions in three different seasons.
    b. He was serving as a Marine aboard the battleship USS Missouri when the Japanese officially surrendered to the Allies on the ship's deck at the end of World War II.
    c. He co-wrote the song "Hound Dog" with legendary rock star Elvis Presley, for which his family receives royalties to this day.
    d. He played or coached under three legendary coaches: Vince Lombardi, Don Shula, and Curly Lambeau.

16. In 1965, Joe Schmidt established the Lions Linebacker Tradition, wherein he donated his gold pocket watch upon

retirement to the next linebacker to take up the mantle for Detroit. To this day, the watch hangs in a linebacker's locker, and he must pass it on if he retires, is traded, cut, or signs elsewhere.

a. True

b. False

17. In 2017, Lions safety Glover Quin promised to donate $100 per tackle and $5,000 per interception to a relief fund for those hit hard by Hurricane Harvey. Which benchmark did his total donation hit that season?

a. $15,000

b. $20,000

c. $25,000

d. $30,000

18. Which of the following is NOT an accurate quote made by someone about legendary Lions linebacker Joe Schmidt?

a. "Virtually invented the middle linebacker position." – Jack Saylor of the Detroit Free Press

b. "If I were to start a team from scratch and pick out just one player, I'd select Joe Schmidt to form the core of my team." – Los Angeles Rams Hall of Fame quarterback Norm Van Brocklin

c. "The best linebacker in the league." – Green Bay Packers Hall of Fame halfback Paul Hornung

d. "He epitomizes everything you could ever want in a football player." – Dallas Cowboys Hall of Fame coach Tom Landry

19. Which Lions linebacker emerged as a Pro Bowl talent in his own right and led the team in tackles for four straight years after backing up superstar left back Chris Spielman during his first season in Detroit?

   a. William White
   b. Stephen Boyd
   c. Stephen Tulloch
   d. Chris Claiborne

20. The NFL's Executive Vice President of Football Operations, Troy Vincent, is Detroit Lions linebacker DeAndre Levy's father-in-law.

   a. True
   b. False

QUIZ ANSWERS

1. D – Dick LeBeau

2. B – False

3. C – Cornerback Lem Barney

4. A – Safety Ron Rice

5. C – Robert William

6. A – Firing an imaginary arrow into the air and watching a teammate pretend to be struck in the heart with it

7. A – True

8. B – In the offseason, he routinely practiced basketball with the Harlem Globetrotters.

9. D – Special assistant to William Clay Ford Sr., Detroit's owner

10. D – He played 23 snaps as a tight end during various games with the Lions.

11. B – 4ᵗʰ overall

12. A – True

13. C – Breaking Penn State coach Joe Paterno's shin in a sideline accident in college

14. D – Jalen Reeves-Maybin

15. C – He co-wrote the song "Hound Dog" with legendary rock star Elvis Presley, for which his family receives royalties to this day.

16. B – False

17. B – $20,000

18. D – "He epitomizes everything you could ever want in a football player." – Dallas Cowboys Hall of Fame coach Tom Landry

19. B – Stephen Boyd

20. A – True

DID YOU KNOW?

1. Passes defended is a stat that the NFL began using at the turn of the century. Cornerback Darius Slay has dominated the statistic for the Lions, having almost 40 more than his closest competition (cornerback Dré Bly).

2. At one point, superstar singer Marvin Gaye attempted to make the Detroit Lions, but he was cut from the team. Gaye had previously become good friends with Lions cornerback Lem Barney after Barney provided background vocals on Gaye's hit song "What's Going On" in 1971.

3. Linebacker Chris Spielman is officially the all-time leading tackler for the Lions franchise. Spielman played in Detroit for eight seasons and racked up over 1,000 tackles during that time. It must be noted though, that the NFL did not keep track of tackles as a statistic during the earlier days of the league's history.

4. Cornerback Dick LeBeau was an NFL lifer. After his Hall of Fame playing career with the Lions, LeBeau developed the zone blitz, which made him a sought after coach and coordinator. LeBeau worked in the NFL for 59 consecutive years before his eventual retirement.

5. Future Lions linebacker Chris Spielman was the first teenager ever to have his picture on a box of the popular breakfast cereal Wheaties. Spielman was given the honor

in 1983 after earning the Dial Award as America's top high school scholar-athlete.

6. Star Lions safety Bennie Blades played all but one of his NFL years with the team. In his last year in the league, 1997, Blades left Detroit to join the Seattle Seahawks so that he could fulfill a dream of being on the same NFL team as his brother, wide receiver Brian Blades.

7. Five defensive backs that have played for the Lions have been enshrined in the Pro Football Hall of Fame. Dick Lane, Yale Larry, Lem Barney, Jack Christiansen, and Dick LeBeau all got the call to the Hall for their distinguished play.

8. Talented Lions safety Jack Christiansen also returned kicks for the club. Christiansen ran back four kicks for touchdowns in 1951, setting an NFL record that has since been matched, but never been broken. Christiansen actually scored those four touchdowns in only two games, getting a pair of scores against both the Los Angeles Rams and the Green Bay Packers that year.

9. Back in the 1950s, two Lions defensive backs set a standard that has yet to be broken. In 1950, Don Doll picked off a dozen passes, establishing the franchise record for a single season. Jack Christiansen nabbed 12 more in 1953 to match the mark, and no one has come close since.

10. Vaunted Lions cornerback Lem Barney is a member of five different Halls of Fame. In addition to the Detroit Lions Hall of Fame and Pro Football Hall of Fame, Barney

also belongs to the Jackson State Sports Hall of Fame and both the Michigan and Mississippi Sports Halls of Fame.

CHAPTER 9:

WHERE'D THEY COME FROM?

QUIZ TIME!

1. Where was popular Lions wide receiver Nate Burleson born?

   a. Flint, Michigan

   b. Dallas, Texas

   c. Manchester, England

   d. Calgary, Alberta

2. Lions wide receiver Calvin Johnson, who played nine years with the team, was born and raised in Detroit, Michigan.

   a. True

   b. False

3. In 1940, the Lions used four of their first five draft picks on players from one college: Doyle Nave, Bill Fisk, Harry Smith, and Bob Winslow. Where did these four athletes go to school?

   a. University of Southern California

   b. University of Notre Dame

c. University of Tennessee

d. University of Oklahoma

4. From which NCAA powerhouse program have the Detroit Lions never selected a player in the 1ˢᵗ round?

   a. Ohio State Buckeyes

   b. Notre Dame Fighting Irish

   c. Clemson Tigers

   d. Louisiana State Tigers

5. From which team did the Lions acquire useful defensive tackle Halotia Ngata in a 2015 swap?

   a. Pittsburgh Steelers

   b. San Diego Chargers

   c. Kansas City Chiefs

   d. Baltimore Ravens

6. Which of the following is NOT an actual college program that Detroit drafted a player from during the 1970 NFL Draft?

   a. Morehead State University

   b. Centenary University

   c. California Polytechnic State University at San Luis Obispo

   d. East West Virginia University

7. The Lions have drafted more players from the Michigan State Spartans than from the Michigan Wolverines over the course of their history.

   a. True

   b. False

8. Which high-profile player dealt in a trade from the Lions to the Denver Broncos went on to return to Detroit with his final contract, though he never played another game for the Lions?

    a. Running back Tatum Bell

    b. Cornerback Dré Bly

    c. Offensive tackle George Foster

    d. Center Graham Glasgow

9. One of the Lions' best recent trades saw them acquire defensive tackle Damon "Snacks" Harrison, in exchange for just a 5th round draft pick. Which team regretted making that deal with Detroit?

    a. Baltimore Ravens

    b. Tennessee Titans

    c. San Francisco 49ers

    d. New York Giants

10. In which city named after a saint was Lions franchise quarterback Bobby Layne born, in 1926?

    a. San Francisco, California

    b. St. Louis, Missouri

    c. Santa Anna, Texas

    d. St. Paul, Minnesota

11. Two players were teammates in college with the University of South Carolina Gamecocks defense before taking the field together in Detroit as well. Which two players were they?

a. Linebacker Boss Bailey and defensive back Keith Smith

b. Defensive ends Jared DeVries and Mike Pringley

c. Defensive end Devin Taylor and linebacker Leon Cunningham

d. Defensive end Kalimba Edwards and defensive back André Goodman

12. Detroit has never in its history completed a trade with the New England Patriots.

a. True

b. False

13. In 2018, the Lions traded star wide receiver Golden Tate to the Philadelphia Eagles. Which pieces did they receive in return?

a. One 3rd round draft choice

b. One 1st round draft choice and one 5th round draft choice

c. Two 2nd round draft choices

d. Two 4th round draft choices and a 6th round draft choice

14. In 1979, the Lions drafted quarterback Jeff Komlo, who played for University of Delaware, in the 9th round. What was his college team's nickname?

a. Sycamores

b. Fightin' Blue Hens

c. Golden Flashes

d. Horned Frogs

15. Larry Woods, chosen 100th overall, played college football as the defensive tackle for which program before coming to the Lions?

    a. Tennessee State Tigers
    b. Clemson Tigers
    c. Louisiana State Tigers
    d. Auburn Tigers

16. In their entire history, the Lions have never traded away a player who was born in the state of Michigan.

    a. True
    b. False

17. Which college program did Lions running back James Jones help lead to one of the greatest one-year recoveries in NCAA history, going from 0-10-1 in 1979 to a bowl game in 1980 after finishing 8-4?

    a. Nebraska Cornhuskers
    b. Southern California Trojans
    c. Washington Huskies
    d. Florida Gators

18. From which rival team did the Lions poach star cornerback Dick Lane in a trade in 1960?

    a. Chicago Cardinals
    b. Washington Redskins
    c. Los Angeles Rams
    d. Green Bay Packers

19. The talented and flamboyant Ndamukong Suh was a member of which college squad before his time on the field with the Lions?

    a. Auburn Tigers
    b. Alabama Crimson Tide
    c. Florida State Seminoles
    d. Nebraska Cornhuskers

20. Detroit has completed more trades with the New York Giants than with any other NFL franchise.

    a. True
    b. False

QUIZ ANSWERS

1. D – Calgary, Alberta

2. B – False

3. A – University of Southern California

4. C – Clemson Tigers

5. D – Baltimore Ravens

6. D – East West Virginia University

7. B – False

8. B – Cornerback Dré Bly

9. D – New York Giants

10. C – Santa Anna, Texas

11. D – Defensive end Kalimba Edwards and defensive back André Goodman

12. B – False

13. A – One 3rd round draft choice

14. B – Fightin' Blue Hens

15. A – Tennessee State Tigers

16. B – False

17. D – Florida Gators

18. A – Chicago Cardinals

19. D – Nebraska Cornhuskers

20. B – False

DID YOU KNOW?

1. When the Lions needed a mentor for young running back D'Andre Swift in 2020, they signed one of the best possible options. Detroit brought on the enormously respected Adrian Peterson, a likely future Hall-of-Famer, by signing him away from the Washington Football Team.

2. University of Oregon coach Len Casanova mailed a letter of intent to Joey Harrington while Harrington was still a baby. Casanova was joking, because Harrington's father had played quarterback at Oregon, and Harrington's grandfather had played quarterback at the nearby University of Portland. However, Harrington did grow up to become a quarterback, did attend Oregon, and was then drafted 3rd overall by the Lions in 2002.

3. The Lions and Chicago Bears have had a fairly heated rivalry throughout their existence, particularly because as divisional opponents, they face each other twice every season. In 2021, with Detroit set to move on from franchise quarterback Matthew Stafford, he was heavily desired by the Bears, who had been adrift without a solid quarterback for a long time. Detroit spurned Chicago's trade offers, though, preferring to send Stafford outside the division to the Los Angeles Rams.

4. On the day before Detroit acquired quarterback Jared Goff from the Los Angeles Rams in 2021, they made a

separate significant trade with Los Angeles that was quickly overshadowed. The Lions acquired veteran defensive lineman Michael Brockers to shore up their line of scrimmage, in exchange for just a 7th round draft choice.

5. In 2006, the Lions finally gave up on the man they thought would be their franchise quarterback, Joey Harrington. Detroit selected Harrington with the 3rd overall pick in 2002, but they never managed to translate his success at the University of Oregon to the NFL. Harrington fetched Detroit just a 5th round draft choice in return when the team sent him to the Miami Dolphins; an indicator of how far his value had fallen.

6. In a decision that was very unpopular at the time, Detroit traded reliable cornerback Darius Slay to the Philadelphia Eagles in 2020 for 3rd and 5th round draft picks. Slay had been to the Pro Bowl for three consecutive seasons at the time of the deal and had never played for a team aside from Detroit in his career.

7. Not many NFL players hail from the continent of Africa, but one of the best called Detroit home while playing defensive end for the Lions. Ezekiel "Ziggy" Ansah was one of just three players from Ghana to ever appear in the league, and he certainly made the biggest impact, becoming the only one to make the Pro Bowl during his career.

8. Hall of Fame center Alex Wojciechowicz is the only player the Lions have ever selected who played in college for the Fordham University Rams.

9. Popular quarterback Dan Orlovsky remains the only University of Connecticut Huskie ever taken by the Lions in an NFL Draft.

10. Detroit hit the jackpot when they selected linebacker Joe Schmidt in the 7th round, 86th overall, in 1953. Schmidt went on to star for the Lions for 13 seasons and was elected to the Pro Football Hall of Fame.

CHAPTER 10:

IN THE DRAFT ROOM

QUIZ TIME!

1. First-ever Lions draft choice Sid Wagner attended Michigan State University, where he played for the football team that went by which nickname?

   a. Pistons
   b. Bruins
   c. Spartans
   d. Wolverines

2. For four consecutive years in the 1990s, the Lions traded out of the 1st round of the NFL Draft, acquiring more proven talent in an effort to compete with the Dallas Cowboys.

   a. True
   b. False

3. The Lions have selected more players from Michigan than any other school. But from which school in the football-crazy state of Texas has Detroit drafted more players?

a. Texas Longhorns

b. Texas Tech Red Riders

c. Texas A&M Aggies

d. Texas El Paso Miners

4. During the 1st round of the 2020 NFL Draft, Detroit congratulated which of the following players on becoming a Lion remotely, via webcam, because of the COVID-19 pandemic that prevented the usual handshakes on stage?

a. Tight end T.J. Hockenson of Iowa

b. Center Frank Ragnow of Arkansas

c. Cornerback Jeff Okudah of Ohio State

d. Running back Kerryon Johnson of Auburn

5. The Lions selected two teammates from the Michigan Wolverines in the 2016 NFL Draft. Which teammates did they choose with the 95th and 191st picks?

a. Defensive tackle A'Shawn Robinson and running back Dwayne Washington

b. Safety Miles Killebrew and defensive tackle Anthony Zettel

c. Linebacker Jarrad Davis and cornerback Teez Tabor

d. Center Graham Glasgow and quarterback Jake Rudock

6. How many times in history has Detroit used a top 10 overall draft pick?

a. 18

b. 29

c. 33

d. 47

7. The Lions have never held the 1ˢᵗ overall pick in the NFL Draft in the entire history of the franchise.

   a. True

   b. False

8. Guard Laken Tomlinson was drafted by the Lions in the 1ˢᵗ round of the 2015 NFL Draft out of which school that is better known as a basketball powerhouse than a football school?

   a. University of North Carolina

   b. Duke University

   c. Gonzaga University

   d. University of Kentucky

9. The 1989 NFL Draft featured four future Hall-of-Famers selected within the first five picks, including legendary Lions running back Barry Sanders. Which of the following players did NOT join him among those picks?

   a. Defensive tackle Cortez Kennedy of the Seattle Seahawks

   b. Quarterback Troy Aikman of the Dallas Cowboys

   c. Cornerback Deion Sanders of the Atlanta Falcons

   d. Linebacker Derrick Thomas of the Kansas City Chiefs

10. Only one Ivy League player lasted 100 games in the NFL after being drafted by the Lions. Which intelligent player made it with Detroit?

a. Defensive tackle Caraun Reid of Princeton University

b. Defensive back Dick Jauron of Yale University

c. Running back Ameer Abdullah of Harvard University

d. Quarterback John Witkowski of Columbia University

11. How high did Detroit select Hall of Fame cornerback Yale Larry in the 1952 NFL Draft?

    a. 1st round, 6th overall

    b. 2nd round, 31st overall

    c. 3rd round, 34th overall

    d. 7th round, 224th overall

12. Due in part to their longstanding rivalry with the Green Bay Packers, Detroit has never drafted a player from the University of Wisconsin.

    a. True

    b. False

13. How many 1st round draft choices have the Lions made in which the player they selected went on to make the Pro Football Hall of Fame?

    a. 0

    b. 2

    c. 7

    d. 9

14. Hall of Fame linebacker Joe Schmidt played four years of college ball for which program before being drafted by the Lions?

a. Pittsburgh Panthers

b. UCLA Bruins

c. Miami Hurricanes

d. Oklahoma Sooners

15. The Lions drafted three players from the Nebraska Cornhuskers who would go on to play more than 170 NFL games each. Who were these players?

   a. Defensive back Ray Crockett, center Kevin Glover, and wide receiver Johnnie Morton

   b. Defensive end Al Baker, tight end David Hill, and kicker Jim Breech

   c. Center Dominic Raiola, fullback Cory Schlesinger, and defensive tackle Ndamukong Suh

   d. Kicker Eddie Murray, linebacker Wally Hilgenberg, and wide receiver Fred Biletnikoff

16. Lions Hall of Fame wide receiver Calvin Johnson was such a talented athlete coming out of college that he was drafted in not one but three sports (basketball, baseball, and football).

   a. True

   b. False

17. Which team did the Lions trade up with so they could select running back Kerryon Johnson at the NFL Draft in 2018?

   a. New England Patriots

   b. Los Angeles Rams

c. New York Jets

d. New York Giants

18. In the 1962 NFL Draft, Detroit selected not one but two quarterbacks, using both their 1st and 2nd round picks to do so. Who did they take to attempt to lock down the position?

   a. Tim Jones from Weber State and Tom Myers from Northwestern

   b. Pete Beathard from Southern California and Joe Zuger from Arizona State

   c. Greg Landry from Massachusetts and Greg Barton from Tulsa

   d. John Hadl from Kansas and Eddie Wilson from Arizona

19. Who did the Detroit Lions select with their two 1st round draft picks in 2010?

   a. Defensive back Amari Spievey and tight end Brandon Pettigrew

   b. Defensive tackle Ndamukong Suh and running back Jahvid Best

   c. Quarterback Matthew Stafford and offensive tackle Gosder Cherilus

   d. Defensive tackle Nick Fairley and offensive tackle Riley Reiff

20. Between 1998 and 2010, Detroit enjoyed a stretch in which they selected at least one player per year who lasted 100

games in the NFL, producing 20 such players during that span.

a. True
b. False

QUIZ ANSWERS

1. C – Spartans

2. B – False

3. A – Texas Longhorns

4. C – Cornerback Jeff Okudah of Ohio State

5. D – Center Graham Glasgow and quarterback Jake Rudock

6. D – 47

7. B – False

8. B – Duke University

9. A – Defensive tackle Cortez Kennedy of the Seattle Seahawks

10. B – Defensive back Dick Jauron of Yale University

11. C – 3rd round, 34th overall

12. B – False

13. C – 7

14. A – Pittsburgh Panthers

15. C – Center Dominic Raiola, fullback Cory Schlesinger, and defensive tackle Ndamukong Suh

16. B – False

17. A – New England Patriots

18. D – John Hadl from Kansas and Eddie Wilson from Arizona

19. B – Defensive tackle Ndamukong Suh and running back Jahvid Best

20. A – True

DID YOU KNOW?

1. Wide receiver Calvin Johnson, who was chosen 2nd overall in 2007 from Georgia Tech, is the highest drafted player the Lions have ever selected who went on to make the Pro Football Hall of Fame.

2. The most players Detroit has drafted from any school is 33. The Lions stayed in their home state for these players, selecting them all from the University of Michigan. The team has mined many good players from the Wolverines' system, but not a single homegrown Hall-of-Famer.

3. In their long history, Detroit has held most picks multiple times, but they have only ever selected 4th overall once. They had mixed results nonetheless, as they selected legendary quarterback and future Hall-of-Famer Otto Graham, but Graham decided to play for the Cleveland Browns instead in the rival All-America Football Conference.

4. Detroit has made two Georgia Bulldogs players the 1st overall pick in the NFL Draft. The team selected back Frank Sinkwich in the top spot in 1943 and quarterback Matthew Stafford first in 2009.

5. In a 21-year span, between 1941 and 1961, the Lions drafted 17 players from local school University of Detroit Mercy. About half of these athletes never played in the NFL, but a handful, such as defensive back Bruce Maher and tackle Grady Alderman, were longtime contributors.

6. Detroit has drafted precisely 20 players who have played a single game in the NFL, including three players from the University of Colorado: tackle Jerry Leahy in 1957, defensive back Lyle Pickens in 1986, and tackle Victor Rogers in 2002.

7. Of the draft spots in the top 10 in the NFL Draft, Detroit has selected at 10th overall more than any other, choosing seven players in that position. Best among them was probably Hall of Fame offensive tackle Alex Karras; although, quarterback John Hadl played more NFL games, and wide receiver Herman Moore was a fixture with the Lions for many years.

8. The smallest number of players ever chosen in a Lions draft class is five. Three times, Detroit had just five selections, including the 1996 class headlined by center Jeff Hartings, the 1998 class led by quarterback Charlie Batch, and the 2011 class that yielded defensive tackle Nick Fairley.

9. The largest Lions draft class ever was selected in 1955, when the team drafted a whopping 33 players over the course of the draft. Just nine of those players suited up for an NFL game, with the team's third choice, defensive end Darris McCord, lasting the longest with a 168-game career.

10. The latest pick the Lions have made in the NFL Draft was defensive back Jim Meeks from Boise State, whom the team chose 475th overall in 1976. Meeks never made it to the NFL. Guard Gordon Jolley, the team's 436th overall

pick from Utah in 1971, was the latest pick they've made who actually played for the team.

CHAPTER 11:

COACHES, GMS, & OWNERS

QUIZ TIME!

1. Who served as the Lions' first general manager?

    a. Dutch Clark

    b. Matt Millen

    c. William Clay Ford

    d. George Richards

2. Detroit general manager Chuck Schmidt once proposed a deal to the New England Patriots that would have sent Lions icon Barry Sanders to Massachusetts in exchange for a young and then little-known Tom Brady.

    a. True

    b. False

3. The Lions' first head coach, Hal Griffen, lasted for how long in that position with the franchise?

    a. 3 games

    b. 1 season

c. 8 seasons

d. 12 seasons

4. The Lions' most recent coach, Dan Campbell, was actually a player for Detroit, where he suited up at which position for the club?

a. Linebacker

b. Offensive tackle

c. Defensive end

d. Tight end

5. Who has owned the Detroit Lions for the longest amount of time?

a. George Richards

b. Edwin Anderson

c. William Clay Ford Sr.

d. Martha Firestone Ford

6. Of all the Detroit bench bosses who have coached over 50 NFL games with the team, which one had the lowest winning percentage at only .310?

a. Darryl Rogers

b. Gus Dorais

c. Jim Schwartz

d. Monte Clark

7. Detroit is the only NFL franchise to have a player rise from competing on the field for the team to ownership of the team.

a. True

b. False

8. Which coach led the Lions to their first NFL championship?

   a. Hal Griffen
   b. Buddy Parker
   c. Wayne Fontes
   d. Potsy Clark

9. Which of the following Detroit general managers only served in the role on an interim basis, but was not selected to hold the job full time?

   a. Sheldon White
   b. Russ Thomas
   c. Martin Mayhew
   d. Bo McMillin

10. Who is Detroit's leader in all-time coaching wins with the franchise?

    a. Potsy Clark
    b. Buddy Parker
    c. Wayne Fontes
    d. Monte Clark

11. The shortest ownership term for a Detroit Lions owner is held by original owner George Richards. For how long did he own the team?

    a. 1 year
    b. 3 years
    c. 9 years
    d. 14 years

12. Two coaches, Dutch Clark and George Wilson, share the benchmark in terms of best winning percentage in a season, as they each led the team to a .786 winning percentage in the regular season, albeit 31 years apart.

    a. True

    b. False

13. How many of the Lions' head coaches have spent their entire NFL coaching career with Detroit?

    a. 2

    b. 6

    c. 10

    d. 17

14. Which Lions general manager has led the franchise to the most playoff appearances, with the team entering the postseason six times under his watch?

    a. Nick Kerbawy

    b. Chuck Schmidt

    c. Matt Millen

    d. Martin Mayhew

15. Out of eight seasons coaching the Lions, how many times did coach George Wilson finish above .500?

    a. 1

    b. 3

    c. 5

    d. 8

16. At one point in their history, the Lions employed four coaches over a decade who had all started for Detroit at some point during their playing careers.

    a. True
    b. False

17. How did Martha Firestone Ford become the majority owner of the Detroit Lions in 2014?

    a. She purchased the team when the previous owners wished to sell.
    b. She inherited the team when her husband, William, died.
    c. She forced a takeover of the corporation that had previously owned the team.
    d. She inherited the team from her father.

18. How many head coaches have roamed the sidelines for the Lions in their history?

    a. 10
    b. 18
    c. 24
    d. 30

19. Which Lions coaches are the only ones to have won an award as the league's top coach, while behind the bench for Detroit?

    a. George Wilson and Wayne Fontes
    b. Dutch Clark and Steve Mariucci
    c. Monte Clark and Jim Schwartz
    d. Gus Dorais and Rod Marinelli

20. Lions owner William Clay Ford Sr. once proposed trading franchises with New York Yankees owner George Steinbrenner, as part of a business deal.

    a. True
    b. False

QUIZ ANSWERS

1. A – Dutch Clark

2. B – False

3. B – 1 season

4. D – Tight end

5. C – William Clay Ford Sr.

6. A – Darryl Rogers

7. B – False

8. D – Potsy Clark

9. A – Sheldon White

10. C – Wayne Fontes

11. B – 3 years

12. A – True

13. D – 17

14. B – Chuck Schmidt

15. C – 5

16. B – False

17. B – She inherited the team when her husband, William, died.

18. D – 30

19. A – George Wilson and Wayne Fontes

20. B – False

DID YOU KNOW?

1. Six times in team history, the Lions have fired a coach midway through a season. The first time occurred in 1942, when Bill Edwards was let go and John Karcis took over. Most recently, it happened in 2020 when the team moved on from Matt Patricia and replaced him (briefly) with Darrell Bevell.

2. Only one man has served as both coach and general manager of the Detroit Lions. Dutch Clark coached the team for two years in 1937 and 1938 and handled the personnel duties for three years, starting in 1936. Since then, the Lions have always had a separation of power at the top of their organization.

3. The Lions have employed three head coaches named Clark. Potsy Clark was at the helm during the 1930s, until Dutch Clark took over during the late 1930s. In 1978, Monte Clark led the squad until his replacement in 1985. The three men were not related.

4. The Lions' original general manager, Dutch Clark, lasted three years in the position before resigning to join the Cleveland Rams. Clark wanted to play for the Rams at the time as well, but the Lions owned his playing rights, and the two teams could not reach a deal for compensation, so Clark remained on the sidelines.

5. As the grandson of automotive innovator Henry Ford, Lions owner William Clay Ford became an executive with the Ford Motor Company, and a very wealthy man. Ford's worth was estimated at $1.4 billion, putting him among the top 400 wealthiest Americans before his death.

6. Head coach Wayne Fontes leads the Detroit Lions with the highest number of both wins (67) and losses (71). He is also the only Lions coach to earn a playoff victory since 1962.

7. Lions coach Jim Schwartz did not win a lot of games with the franchise, but he sure could coach defense. Every time Schwartz had a head coaching gig or defensive coordinator position in the NFL, his teams sent a defensive tackle to the Pro Bowl or onto the All-Pro Team. This included Albert Haynesworth with the Tennessee Titans, Ndamukong Suh with the Lions, Marcell Dareus with the Buffalo Bills, and Fletcher Cox with the Philadelphia Eagles.

8. The Lions beat the New England Patriots during the 2000 season, and then not again for 18 years. In 2018, they hired ex-Patriots coach Matt Patricia as their head coach, and Patricia's inside knowledge of his former club led to a 26-10 victory to snap the streak.

9. Matt Millen was an unpopular choice as general manager for the Lions. Millen presided over eight seasons with the club, during which Detroit finished with a 31-84 record that was last in the NFL. This included a losing season, at 0-16, during which Millen was relieved of his duties.

10. In league history, Detroit general managers have never been awarded the Sporting News NFL Executive of the Year Award. In fairness, the award has been given continuously since 1972, and all of Detroit's championship seasons happened in the decades prior to its creation.

CHAPTER 12:

ODDS & ENDS

QUIZ TIME!

1. Which Lion has won the most league MVP trophies while playing for Detroit?

    a. Quarterback Bobby Layne

    b. Wide receiver Calvin Johnson

    c. Quarterback Matthew Stafford

    d. Running back Barry Sanders

2. The first Lion to win any major award given out by the NFL was franchise tight end Charlie Sanders.

    a. True

    b. False

3. During which season did the Lions win their first NFL Championship trophy?

    a. 1935

    b. 1952

    c. 1991

    d. 2004

4. In 2019, the NFL announced its All-Time Team, recognizing the 100 greatest players from the first 100 years of NFL history. How many of these players suited up for the Lions?

    a. 1 on offense, 1 on defense, and 1 on special teams
    b. 2 on offense, 3 on defense, and 0 on special teams
    c. 3 on offense, 1 on defense, and 2 on special teams
    d. 2 on offense, 5 on defense, and 1 on special teams

5. What negative event befell quarterback Matthew Stafford before he returned to the Lions and won the 2011 Comeback Player of the Year Award?

    a. A concussion suffered early in the previous year
    b. A lymphoma diagnosis, which caused Stafford to miss 11 games and most of the following training camp
    c. A shoulder injury the season before that required surgery to repair
    d. A rare case of amnesia brought on by a car accident that left Stafford unable to remember the playbook

6. What is Dan Miller's connection to the Detroit Lions?

    a. An architect who designed and built Ford Field for the Lions
    b. A beloved groundskeeper who has worked for the Lions since 1981
    c. A player agent who represented Matthew Stafford, Calvin Johnson, and several others

d. A longtime radio play by play announcer for the Lions on their home station

7. The Detroit Lions/Portsmouth Spartans have the most wins of any franchise in NFL history.

   a. True
   b. False

8. Hall of Fame Lions running back Doak Walker won the Heisman Trophy while playing where?

   a. University of Oklahoma
   b. University of Michigan
   c. Duke University
   d. Southern Methodist University

9. How many players have ever won the NFL's Defensive Player of the Year Award while playing for the Detroit Lions?

   a. 0
   b. 1: Linebacker Joe Schmidt
   c. 2: Linebacker Joe Schmidt and cornerback Dick LeBeau
   d. 4: Linebacker Joe Schmidt, defensive tackle Ndamukong Suh, and cornerbacks Dick LeBeau and Dick Lane

10. Only one Lions defensive player played an entire career of at least 15 years for the Lions without ever starting a game for another NFL franchise. Which loyal athlete played only for Detroit for 15 seasons?

a. Linebacker Chris Spielman

b. Defensive end Robert Porcher

c. Safety Bennie Blades

d. Linebacker Wayne Walker

11. Quarterback Earl Morrall joined the Lions in 1958, the season *after* they won a championship. But Morrall went on to be a key member of four championship teams with which two other franchises?

a. Pittsburgh Steelers and Minnesota Vikings

b. Green Bay Packers and Kansas City Chiefs

c. Baltimore Colts and Miami Dolphins

d. Washington Redskins and Chicago Bears

12. Detroit is the first NFL team to win the Super Bowl after losing the previous year.

a. True

b. False

13. How far did Bill Sheppard boot the longest punt in Lions history?

a. 72 yards

b. 78 yards

c. 81 yards

d. 85 yards

14. Of the Lions in the Football Hall of Fame, running back Dutch Clark is first among them to play with the franchise. What year did he begin playing with the team?

a. 1931

b. 1934

c. 1945

d. 1957

15. Only one Lion has ever been named the NFL's Offensive Player of the Year, but he won the award twice. Who received that honor?

a. Running back Barry Sanders in 1994 and 1997

b. Quarterback Matthew Stafford in 2011 and 2016

c. Wide receiver Calvin Johnson in 2009 and 2013

d. Tailback Dutch Clark in 1928 and 1933

16. Kicker Jason Hanson has *missed* more field goals during his Lions career than any other Detroit player has even *attempted*.

a. True

b. False

17. Which Lions kicker (with at least 50 kicks attempted) holds the team's highest field goal percentage, at 84.4% made?

a. Jason Hanson

b. Eddie Murray

c. Errol Mann

d. Matt Prater

18. Which of the following is NOT true about longtime Lions long snapper Don Muhlbach?

a. General Manager Matt Millen once called Muhlbach "the Nolan Ryan of long snappers."

b. Since 2005, Muhlbach has played in every Lions game except for one, which he missed with a concussion.

c. Muhlbach has never been part of another NFL team during his playing career.

d. As of the start of the 2021 season, Muhlbach still isn't the oldest player in the league, four years behind Tampa Bay Buccaneers quarterback Tom Brady.

19. How did linebacker Reggie Brown suffer the injury that put an end to his NFL career?

a. Suffered a spinal cord contusion while making a tackle in a Lions game

b. Fell asleep while driving and crashed his vehicle

c. Shot in the leg during an armed robbery at the team's hotel

d. Broke a vertebra while diving into shallow water on vacation

20. The Lions have never played in a Super Bowl game, although they have won NFL Championships.

a. True

b. False

QUIZ ANSWERS

1. D – Running back Barry Sanders

2. B – False

3. A – 1935

4. B – 2 on offense, 3 on defense, and 0 on special teams

5. C – A shoulder injury the season before that required surgery to repair

6. D – A longtime radio play by play announcer for the Lions on their home station

7. B – False

8. D – Southern Methodist University

9. A – 0

10. D – Linebacker Wayne Walker

11. C – Baltimore Colts and Miami Dolphins

12. B – False

13. D – 85 yards

14. A – 1931

15. A – Running back Barry Sanders in 1994 and 1997

16. B – False

17. D – Matt Prater

18. C – Muhlbach has never been part of another NFL team during his playing career

19. A – Suffered a spinal cord contusion while making a tackle in a Lions game

20. A – True

DID YOU KNOW?

1. Kicker Matt Prater holds the franchise record for the longest field goal ever made by a Lion. His record-setting kick came on August 23, 2019, in a close 24-20 loss to the Buffalo Bills. Prater nailed a 61-yard attempt at the end of the first half of the preseason finale to set the mark. However, officially, Prater's 59-yard kick on January 3, 2016, against the Bears is the longest in franchise history.

2. Detroit was the beneficiary of a controversial referee decision in a 1998 Thanksgiving Day game against the Pittsburgh Steelers. When the game went to overtime, Pittsburgh's Jerome Bettis called "tails" for the coin toss, but the referee heard "heads" and gave Detroit the ball. The Lions scored to win the game without Pittsburgh ever gaining possession.

3. Lions icon Jason Hanson ranks fourth on the all-time list for most field goals made in the history of the NFL. Hanson converted 495 between 1992 and 2012 for Detroit, placing him behind only Adam Vinatieri, Morten Andersen, and Gary Anderson for the lead.

4. Detroit has a winning record against six other current NFL teams. The Lions have gotten the better of the Cleveland Browns, Jacksonville Jaguars, New York Giants, Atlanta Falcons, Arizona Cardinals, and Tampa Bay Buccaneers.

5. The nickname's value is estimated at $2.1 billion by *Forbes* magazine, which ranks them as the 30th most valuable NFL team, right between the Tampa Bay Buccaneers and the Buffalo Bills.

6. The Lions have played more games against the Chicago Bears than any other team in the NFL. The two clubs have faced off 182 times, with Detroit holding a 75-102-5 record all time, good for a .426 winning percentage.

7. In 1967, the Lions were able to boast that they had both the Offensive *and* Defensive Rookie of the Year. Running back Mel Farr took home the award on offense, and cornerback Lem Barney was granted the hardware on defense.

8. Two high school teammates would also go on to become teammates with the Detroit Lions. Quarterback Bobby Layne and running back Doak Walker both starred for Highland Park High School in Texas, and then reunited as professionals where they both won NFL Championships and were elected to the Pro Football Hall of Fame.

9. Only one player in NFL history has passed away while playing in an actual game. Sadly, this was Lions wide receiver Chuck Hughes, who collapsed due to a blocked artery while facing the Chicago Bears in 1971. The game, incredibly, was finished anyway, with the Lions losing 28-23.

10. Lions kicker Jason Hanson set the NFL record for the most professional seasons played for a single team in 2012. Hanson suited up for Detroit (and only Detroit) every year

from 1992 to 2012, lasting an incredible 21 seasons with the club.

CONCLUSION

There you have it; an amazing collection of Lions trivia, information, and statistics at your fingertips! Regardless of how you fared on the quizzes, we hope that you found this book entertaining, enlightening, and educational.

Ideally, you knew many of these details, but also learned a good deal more about the history of the Detroit Lions; their players, coaches, management; and some of the quirky stories surrounding the team. If you got a little peek into the colorful details that make being a fan so much more enjoyable, then mission accomplished!

The good news is, the trivia doesn't have to stop there! Spread the word. Challenge your fellow Lions fans to see if they can do any better. Share some of the stories with the next generation to help them become Detroit supporters too.

If you are a big enough Lions fan, consider creating your own quiz with some of the details you know that weren't presented here, and then test your friends to see if they can match your knowledge.

The Detroit Lions are a storied franchise. They have a long history with multiple periods of success, and a few that were less than successful. They've had glorious superstars, iconic moments, and hilarious tales. But most of all, they have wonderful, passionate fans. Thank you for being one of them.

Made in the USA
Monee, IL
20 November 2024

70657841R00075